NUMBER MAGIC

Illustrated by A. Howe

1 MAGIC NUMBERS

Ask someone to think of the number of the month in which they were born; so January would be 1, February = 2, and so on. Multiply it by 2; add 5; multiply that by 50; add his age; subtract 365; add 115; now ask the result.

The last two numbers will reveal his age, and the first two will reveal the month. For instance, if the result was 645 - 45 is the age, and 6 is the month, being June.

2 AUDIENCE AGE

Before you perform this trick, study the chart but don't tell your audience how you work out the answer. They'll be astonished!
By using this chart you will be able to tell the age of anyone in your audience, as long as they are under 64 years old (perhaps you had better not invite Gran to play.)
Show the chart and ask them to tell you in which columns their age appears. Add up the first number in each of those columns indicated. This will tell you the correct age. For example, if someone points to the 2nd, 3rd and 5th columns, their age must be 22!

Answers to all puzzles can be found at the back of this book, starting on page 45.

CHART FOR AUDIENCE AGE

1	2	4	8	16	32
3	3	5	9	17	33
5	6	6	10	18	34
7	7	7	11	19	35
9	10	12	12	20	36
11	11	13	13	21	37
13	14	14	14	22	38
15	15	15	15	23	39
17	18	20	24	24	40
19	19	21	25	25	41
21	22	22	26	26	42
23	23	23	27	27	43
25	26	28	28	28	44
27	27	29	29	29	45
29	30	30	30	30	46
31	31	31	31	31	47
33	34	36	40	48	48
35	35	37	41	49	49
37	38	38	42	50	50
39	39	39	43	51	51
41	42	44	44	52	52
43	43	45	45	53	53
45	46	46	46	54	54
47	47	47	47	55	55
49	50	52	56	56	56
51	51	53	57	57	57
53	54	54	58	58	58
55	55	55	59	59	59
57	58	60	60	60	60
59	59	61	61	61	61
61	62	62	62	62	62
63	63	63	63	63	63

3 TAP IT

Write this number table clearly onto a piece of paper. Show it to a friend. Ask that person now to THINK of any number he sees written on the paper. Beginning with one number above the number he is thinking of, he is to start counting (mentally) as you, the magician, tap on the number with a pencil - or wand. One count for each tap. He is to say “Stop” when his mental counting reaches twenty. On the count of twenty, the magician’s pencil is tapping the number the person first thought of.

9	2	8	6
7	12	3	10
1	4	11	5

4 IS IT ODD ... OR EVEN?

This is a card trick which will have your audience fooled - but don't perform it twice for the same people.
Hand cards from an ordinary pack to one of your audience, saying, "I will hand you cards, two at a time, and I want you to make two even piles. Then I will hand you one card and you make whichever pile you wish - odd."
When it's done, you continue,"Pick up the odd pile and hand me two cards at a time, but you keep the odd card." Spectator finds to his astonishment that the pile he thought was odd is EVEN, and the pile he thought was even is ODD.
How it's done: When you hand over the cards, pass him nine sets of two's, then hand him one card. Now the pile that he thinks he is making odd is really even, (ten cards are in that pile). It is the other pile that is odd (nine cards).

5 FORCE THE NO. 9

Ask someone to take three different numbers, reverse them, and then to subtract the small set of figures from the larger. The middle figure will always be 9. Sometimes the answer will come out in two figures. In that case, the answer will always be 99. Tell them to take either figure.

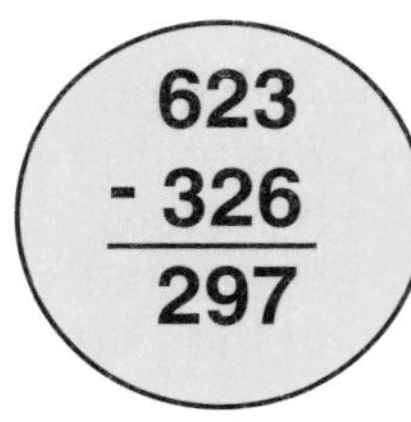

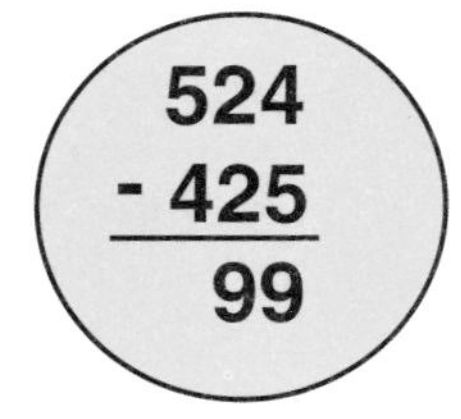

6 UPSIDE DOWN

Write the figures below on a blank sheet of paper and ask your friends if the addition is correct. When they say it is wrong, turn it upside down and prove it is correct!

7 FUNNY BANK NOTES

Here's a clever one. Try this on your friends and see how many wrong answers you get!

A boy buys a book for £3.00 at the market. He gives the bookseller a £10.00 note. The bookseller goes to the fruit stall to have it changed; when he comes back, he gives the boy £7.00.

Later that morning, the stall keeper from the fruit stall comes to the bookstand and says, "That was a fake bank note you gave me." The bookseller gives him a good bank note.

How much is the bookseller out?

8 MAGIC NUMBERS

Challenge your friends to make eight 8's total 1000. It isn't at all easy if you don't know the solution which we have shown you below.

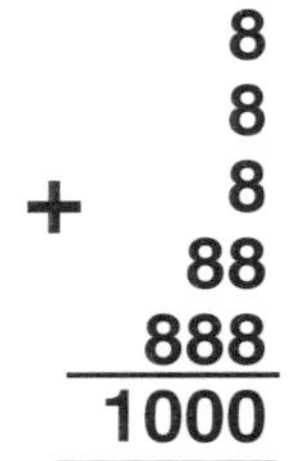

9 CROSS-NUMBER PUZZLE

Here is a seemingly simple puzzle which is not quite as simple as it appears. Draw a form of nine squares. Ask your friends to fill it with numbers from 1 to 9, without repeating any number, so that the numbers will total 15 when added vertically, horizontally and diagonally.
Don't let them see the solution until they have given in or got it right!

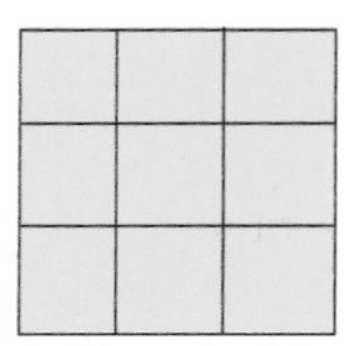

10 DICEY BUSINESS

Using three dice, ask a friend to roll them while you have your back turned. He should total the three numbers that come up. Now tell him to turn over any one of the dice and add the bottom number. Now ask him to throw the same dice he turned over and add whatever number comes up. You turn around and name the total.

The secret is: Just add seven to the total

11 PENNIES TO POUNDS !?!

Copy the picture above onto a piece of paper, but make it larger scale. Place four large coins (we'll call these pounds) in the boxes on the **left** and four smaller coins (we'll call these pennies) in the squares on the **right**, as our picture shows. (You could use any coins as long as four are of lesser value that the other four).

The problem is to transpose the coins so that the pound coins shall be in the **right** hand spaces, by the following rules:

1. Each coin can be moved only one space at a time.

2. If a coin is divided from a vacant square by a single coin of another value, it may jump over it into that square.

3. Coins may be moved in a forward direction only, that is, pounds to the right, pennies to the left . A move once made cannot be retraced.

12 MATCHING PAIRS

A card trick - with a difference.
The object is to 'predict' when a volunteer from your audience will tell you to stop dealing. Put the nine of Clubs on top of the pack and the three of Diamonds on the bottom before you start.

1. Say you will pick two cards to match the ones he chooses when he stops you dealing. Take the three of Hearts and the nine of Spades. Lay them face down, without showing them.

2. Start dealing the cards face-down, asking your volunteer to say "stop". When he does, lay the three of Hearts face-up on the dealt cards, and put the rest of the pack on top of the three of Hearts.

3. Now start dealing from the top of the pack again, asking the volunteer when to stop. This time put the nine of Spades face-up on the top of the dealt cards and the rest of the pack on the top again.

4. Remind the volunteer that you chose your cards before dealing. Take the three of Hearts and nine of Spades out of the pack with the card above each of them. Reveal the matching pairs.

13 IN ADDITION

In this super sized addition sum each row consists of the ten digits 0 to 9. Add them all together and guess what you get in the answer!

```
0 1 2 3 4 5 6 7 8 9
0 2 4 6 9 1 3 5 7 8
0 4 9 3 8 2 7 1 5 6
0 6 1 7 2 8 3 9 4 5
0 8 6 4 1 9 7 5 2 3   +
0 9 8 7 6 5 4 3 1 2
1 2 3 4 5 6 7 8 9 0
1 6 0 4 9 3 8 2 5 7
1 9 7 5 3 0 8 6 2 4
1 7 2 8 3 9 5 1 3 6
___________________

___________________
```

14 IT'S IN THE BAG

Tom goes to his pal Tim and gives him 25 pennies and six paper bags. Tom asks Tim to put an odd number of pennies into each of the bags so that no pennies are left over.

It shouldn't be possible to put an odd number into an even number of bags, sacks or whatever you like AND for the total to be an odd number.

Oddly enough, Tim managed to do it. How?

15 HEADS YOU LOSE

Here's an out and out sneaky trick! You'll need a piece of paper with a straight line drawn on it, along with three coins. The challenge is to put the coins on the paper so that there are two heads on one side of the line and two tails on the other side. Two heads and two tails, surely that makes four coins in all! How can you do it with three?

Easy! Place one coin 'heads' upwards on the paper. Place another coin 'tails' upward on the paper. Move these so that they are on different sides of the line. Then take the third coin and place it on its edge on the line. Heads to face the direction of the coin lying flat and showing heads. Use the first two coins to help the third coin stand up if you need to.

16 WELL BALANCED

The sums below form a well-balanced pattern. Solve the sums and see what the answers look like.

$1 \times 9 + 2 =$ ______

$12 \times 9 + 2 =$ ______

$123 \times 9 + 4 =$ ______

$1234 \times 9 + 5 =$ ______

$12345 \times 9 + 6 =$ ______

$123456 \times 9 + 7 =$ ______

$1234567 \times 9 + 8 =$ ______

$12345678 \times 9 + 9 =$ ______

$123456789 \times 9 + 10 =$ ______

17 PIECES OF EIGHT

A number contains eight digits. There are two 1's, two 2's, two 3's and two 4's. The 1's are separated by one digit, the 2's by two digits, the 3's by three digits and the 4's by four digits. What number is it?

18 CRAFTY CARDS

Ask a friend to think of any number between 1 and 90. They must keep the number a secret, but you will be able to work out that number every time ... with the help of these number cards.

Show all the seven cards to your friend. They in turn point out to you each card that contains the number they thought of. Now you can reach their number by adding together all the top left corner numbers on cards returned to you.

For example: **38** is the chosen number. It appears on the card with **32** top left, on the card with **4** top left and on the card with **2** top left.

32 + 4 + 2 = 38.

This will work every time unless your mate forgets to indicate all the cards (or if your addition goes wrong!).

CRAFTY CARDS

1	25	47	69
3	27	49	71
5	29	51	73
7	31	53	75
9	33	55	77
11	35	57	79
13	37	59	81
15	39	61	83
17	41	63	85
19	43	65	87
21	45	67	89
23			

32	40	48	56
33	41	49	57
34	42	50	58
35	43	51	59
36	44	52	60
37	45	53	61
38	46	54	62
39	47	55	63

64	71	78	85
65	72	79	86
66	73	80	87
67	74	81	88
68	75	82	89
69	76	83	90
70	77	84	

4	23	46	69
5	28	47	70
6	29	52	71
7	30	53	76
12	31	54	77
13	36	55	78
14	37	60	79
15	38	61	84
20	39	62	85
21	44	63	86
22	45	68	87

2	26	47	70
3	27	50	71
6	30	51	74
7	31	54	75
10	34	55	78
11	35	58	79
14	38	59	82
15	39	62	83
18	42	63	86
19	43	66	87
22	46	67	90
23			

16	27	54	81
17	28	55	82
18	29	56	83
19	30	57	84
20	31	58	85
21	48	59	86
22	49	60	87
23	50	61	88
24	51	62	89
25	52	63	90
26	53	80	

8	27	46	73
9	28	47	74
10	29	56	75
11	30	57	76
12	31	58	77
13	40	59	78
14	41	60	79
15	42	61	88
24	43	62	89
25	44	63	90
26	45	72	

19 21 TODAY

Challenge someone to take six digits from the list and put them together in a single column, so that all six will add together to form exactly 21. It looks easy enough, but wait and see!
Set a time limit if you like ... because there's just no way to do it!

1 1 1

3 3 3

5 5 5

7 7 7

9 9 9

20 TIME TRIP

In the year 1961 the date looked the same whether looked at normally or turned upside down! Which was the last year before 1961 in which the same thing happened?

21 TOP MARKS

Here are four marks. Can you put down five more marks to make ten?

22 FAKE A TAKEAWAY

Here's how to prove that well-known sum of 4 minus 4 equals 8. Yes, that's right, 4 - 4 = 8. Most bright sparks will chirp in and say that 4 - 4 = 0, and that's the moment you choose to prove how it makes 8.

Take a piece of paper. Whatever size it is, it will have four corners. Tear a triangle out of each corner as shown.

When you started out there were four corners. You have taken away four corners. Now there are eight corners - see? Four minus four do equal eight!

23 NINE'S FINE

This is how to provide an answer before you even know what the sum is!
You need someone to baffle with your amazing knowledge, a pencil, a sheet of paper and a calculator.

1 Without anyone seeing, write down the number **9** on a piece of paper.
2 Now ask someone to think of any number between **10 and 98**. The only 'no-go' numbers are repeat digits, eg. **11, 22, 55, 88.**
Let's take **65** for an example.
3 Your friend reverses the digits. So, **65** becomes **56**.
4 The smaller number is taken from the larger number **(65 - 56 = 9**)
5 Your friend must return to his original number and find the difference between the two digits. **(In 65, 6 - 5 = 1**).
6 Divide the number arrived at in stage **4** by the number arrived at in stage **5**,
(9 divided by 1 = 9)
7 Now ask your mate to look at the piece of paper. Tell them it will contain the answer to their sum. And - of course - it does. The answer will always be **9**.

24 JOIN THE DOTS

No problem joining the dots together, but can you join them by using just four straight lines, without taking your pencil off the page?

25 THE SECRET SQUARE

A 'mind reading' trick that involves paper, pencil - and a mate who is ready to be fooled.

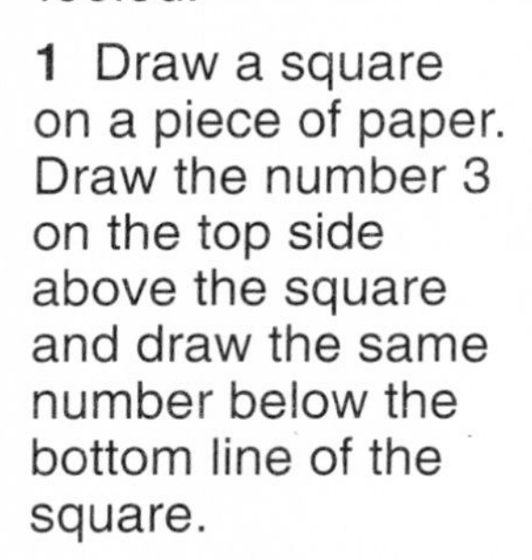

1 Draw a square on a piece of paper. Draw the number 3 on the top side above the square and draw the same number below the bottom line of the square.

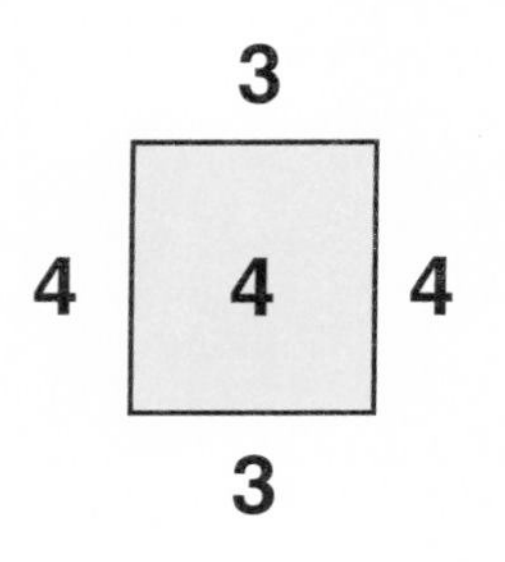

2 Ask your friend to think of a number from 1 to 9 and write that number inside the square. They then write the same number outside the square, both to the left side and the right side

3 There will now be five numbers on the piece of paper. Get your friend to add them all together and tell you the total.

4 You now 'mind read' and name the number that your friend thought of. All you have to do is divide your friend's total by 3 and then take away 2 from the answer eg. your friend selects 4. On the paper 4 will be written three times, and 3 written twice. 4 + 4 + 4 + 3 + 3 = 18. Divide 18 by 3 to give 6, then take away the 2 to give 4.

If your friend chose 9, then the total would be 33 (9 + 9 + 9 + 3 = 33), divide by 3 to give 11, then take the 2 away to give 9.

26 CODE BUSTER

Here is a tricky code for you to decipher. Allocate the numbers 1 to 26 to the letters of the alphabet, ie. A = 1, B = 2 to Z = 26. Then, find which of the following is the odd one out.

a) 12212451321521187
b) 2512792113
c) 14520851812114419
d) 45141311811
e) 61811435
f) 6914121144
g) 92011225

27 CLOCKWISE

This clock is being viewed in a mirror. What is the correct time?

28 MORE NUMBERS

Which number should appear on the last circle?

29 MATHIMAGICIAN

This trick requires 2 sheets of paper, an envelope, a pencil - and an audience.

The idea is to create the impression of knowing the answer to a sum that a person in your audience hasn't even thought of!

Telling your audience about your special powers of mind-reading. Suddenly, point to one spectator. Pretend to receive thoughts transmitted from that person's mind. (You'll have everyone glued to their seats!) Then, rush to a piece of paper (conveniently placed nearby,) and write down 1089. Fold it so no-one reads the number, put it in the envelope, and seal it.

Hand the other piece of paper to your chosen spectator.
Ask them to write a 3 figure number in which each figure is different - then to reverse that number, then, to take the smaller number from the larger one.
Next, they write down that answer as 3 digits, even if the first is 0.
Again, they reverse the number and add these two final figures together.
Ask them to read their answer aloud. With great theatrical flourish you offer them the envelope to open and read the number.
Both will say 1089.

30 NUMBER TRICKERY

Here's a trick you can perform to an audience. Try it out on your classmates, but first you must prepare it with an accomplice!

You will need to devise a simple code, like the example used below:

1=1, 2=go, 3=can, 4=what, 5=quick, 6=please, 7=will, 8=now, 9=right,

Then, ask a member of your audience to write down a single number on a slip of paper and hand it to you. Your accomplice, meanwhile, stands at the back of the room - a blindfold adds effect to this trick.

Now, remembering the secret code you both practised, you describe the number on the paper like this:

Ask, "**What** is this number?" (Your accomplice will know it's **4**).

"**Now**, what is this next number?" (The answer should be **84**).

Try this with numbers on cards, coins or birthdates. If you both know your codes back to front, you'll amaze and puzzle your audience!

MORE NUMBER TRICKERY

The number seven has always been linked with magical powers. There is evidence of this right back to ancient Egypt.
Back to the present, though - there are some calculations which, if you work them out, all have the answer 7.

Take this further and try a trick on a friend. Ask your friend to tap any number into a calculator, then write it on paper. (The number should be at least one digit less than the number of digits which can be shown on the calculator screen.)

Now give these instructions:

Multiply the number by 2 (use a calculator)

Add 5

Add 12

Subtract 3

Divide the answer by 2.

Subtract the first number (remember, this is also on the paper).

Here comes the answer - Magic Seven!

31 TRICK QUESTION

There is a trick involved here, but the puzzle is possible to solve. **Here it is: from 19 take one away and leave 20**

32 MISSING NUMBER

50400, 7200, 900, 100, ?

33 YOU'RE A GENIUS!

Here are some number puzzles that will test you!

1.Two figures are represented here by the letters A and B.

If B +AB = A x A, what are the two figures?

Sounds horrid? Well, here's a clue; one of the figures is 8.

2.How many ones are there in eleven million, one hundred and one thousand and eleven?

3.Try this sum in Roman numerals!

X + X - III - IV + XII - IX + VII =

4.And now, to test your powers of concentration, can you work out the sum below, in your head?

Begin with 4. Double it. Take away 3. Double it. Divide by 5. Add 68. Multiply by 3. Take away 30. Divide by 3. Take away 12. Divide by 4. Add 30. Halve it. Add 4. Multiply by 4. Treble it. What's the answer?

34 MAGIC STAR

Here's one for bright sparks who like addition! Can you arrange numbers from 1 to 12 such that the total of the number in any one line is the same?
What are the missing numbers?

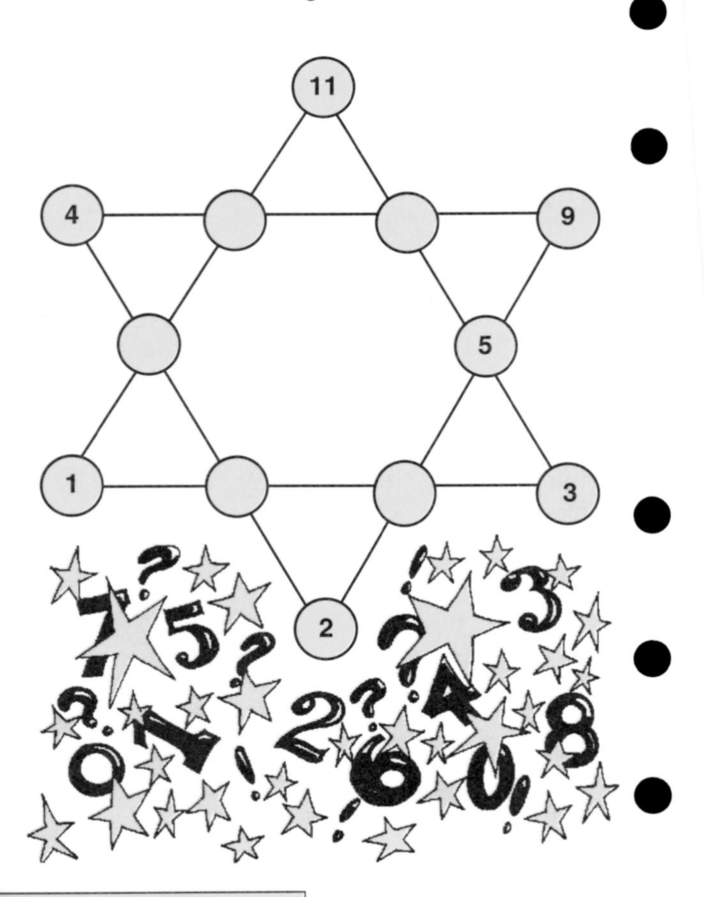

35 MAGIC SQUARE

Fill up the sixteen squares with numbers from 1 to 16. Each number may only be used once. The total sum of numbers in any row, column or diagonal must be the same.

1	15		14
			7
		16	
8		5	11

36 VANISHING SQUARES

These five squares have been made using 16 matchsticks.
Can you reduce the number of squares to four, moving only two matchsticks? You can't overlap a matchstick and there must be no loose or open ends.

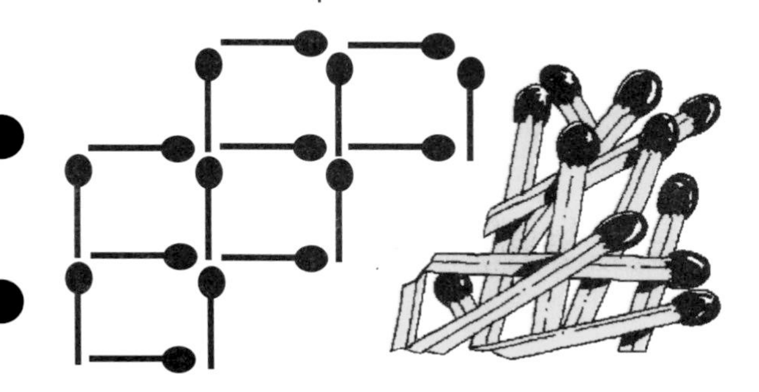

37 MAGIC SEVEN

A magician had seven daughters and they each had a brother. How many children did the magician have?

38 SQUARE MAGIC

We have used 20 sticks to build these 7 boxes. We challenge you to move just 4 sticks in order to reduce the number of boxes to 5. You can't overlap any sticks and no loose ends are allowed, either. Can you do it?

39 NUMBER FUN

In the sum on the blackboard, each letter stands for a 1-digit number other than 0 and 9. The value of "SIX" is greater than the value of "TWO" and "X" is the odd number.

There - we've given you enough information. Now can you work out what number is represented by each letter on the board? Hands up with the right answer!

40 MULTIPLICATION

How good is your multiplication? It's hard enough just reading the word, isn't it! Have a close look at our sum. One of the digits is wrong. Which one is it?

24 X 13 = 377

41 MAGIC 6 AND 9

Here's a very special Magic Square. All the numbers are made up of the digits 6 and 9 only. No number is repeated and the missing numbers are all 4-digit numbers. Like other Magic Squares in this book, each row, column or diagonal must add up to the same total.
It really is extraordinary ....!
If you succeed , you will soon see that the numbers follow a certain pattern. If you invert the completed square, you will discover another Magic Square!

9969		9699	
			6669
6966	9669	6696	
6699		6969	9666

42 MAGIC SQUARE 5 X 5

This square consists of numbers from 1 to 25. Each row, column or diagonal must add up to the same total but no number must be used more than once.

17	24		8	
			14	
4		13		
		19	21	3
11	18	25		

43 UPSIDE DOWN MAGIC

A Magic Square with a difference! The missing numbers you need are all 4-digit numbers taken from 1, 0, 6, 8 and 9. Any row, column or diagonal of numbers must have the same total.

But that's not all - once you have used your genius to find the numbers, turn this Magic Square upside down and, hey presto! .... another Magic Square appears!

	1886		
6961	9109		1088
9806		1981	
	8911		6866

44 LAUGHING ROMANS

An Ancient Roman named Polybius, devised a code for sending important secret messages. He used a grid of 25 squares, like the one below.

COLUMNS

ROWS	1	2	3	4	5
1	A	B	C	D	E
2	F	G	H	I	J
3	K	L	M	N	O
4	P	Q	R	S	T
5	U	V	W	XY	Z

To send a message, he would use numbers instead of letters, giving the row first, then the column position second. So, J is written as 25, (row 2, column 5,) while S becomes 44.

Using Polybius' square above, can you crack this joke? (It's an old one - the Romans used to tell it!)

33 54 14 35 22 23 11 44
34 35 34 35 44 15 23 35 53
14 35 15 44 23 15
44 33 15 32 32
45 15 43 43 24 12 15

45 WHAT'S MY AGE?

You will need a pocket calculator for this next trick. The idea is to reveal someone's age, without them telling you. Try this on an adult, like a teacher, perhaps?

Give your calculator to that person - and ask them to follow your instructions. Now read each step aloud, from the list below:

Step 1 Key in your age
Step 2 x 5
Step 3 + 5
Step 4 x 2
Step 5 + 5
Step 6 x 10

Now ask for the calculator again, with the number still in the display.
Step 7 You subtract 87 from that number shown.
Step 8 Then, remove the last two digits from the number left.
Hey Presto! This final number is their age, which you have discovered - as if by magic

46 FIVE'S ALIVE

You might just want a calculator for this poser - but if you haven't got one, try working it out on paper.

Here's a bunch of fives! Count the fives, multiplying the total each time you count a number. **(5 x 5 = 25. 25 x 5 = 125, and so on).**
What's the final total?

47 CALCULATOR-CLEVER

Here's some number magic to show your friends! Ask a friend to think of a number up to 5 digits, and key it into a calculator - without showing you.
Then ask your friend to follow these steps:

1. Multiply by 5
2. Plus 25
3. Multiply by 5
4. Plus 35
5. Multiply by 4

Now ask for the calculator, with the final figure still on the display.

The work is now up to you!

Subtract 640 from the total.
Remove the last 2 digits and you will have found the very number your friend thought of!

48 BACKCHAT

Did you know that a calculator can make words as well as numbers?
If you work out the answers to the puzzles below, then turn your calculator *upside down* , you will find the calculator has written a word, in each case!

A. 888.5 x 8 =
B. 13527 ÷ 3 =
C. 25101776 ÷ 632 =
D. 643 x 5 =
E. 115374 ÷ 123 =

49 COUNTING COWS

You don't have to be a magician to solve this puzzle - just a wizard at maths!

Farmer Herbert has had a busy day!
By the time he had made five journeys, his trailer had carried a total of 500 cows.
(That's a lot of bull!)
There were 190 cows altogether on the first two trips; 155 cows altogether on the second and third trips; 210 cows altogether on the third and fourth trips; and 225 cows altogether on the fourth and fifth trips.

How many cows were on the trailer on the third trip?

50 NINE'S EASY

This is a most unusual way to learn your Nine Times Table! Here's how it works.

For example, to work out 4 x 9, look at number four on the outside of the ring, then read across the wiggly line to the numbers inside the ring. Answer - 36.

To test it out, try these:

2 x 9 =
3 x 9 =
5 x 9 =
6 x 9 =
7 x 9 =
8 x 9 =

ANSWERS

5. Funny Bank Notes
£7 - and the book!

9. Cross Number Puzzle

8	3	4
1	5	9
6	7	2

11. Pennies to Pounds
6 to 5, 4 to 6, 3 to 4, 5 to 3, 7 to 5, 8 to 7, 6 to 8;
4 to 6, 2 to 4, 1 to 2, 3 to 1, 5 to 3, 7 to 5, 9 to 7, 8 to 9;
6 to 8, 4 to 6, 2 to 4, 3 to 2, 5 to 3, 7 to 5, 6 to 7, 4 to 6,
5 to 4, = Solved.

13. In Addition
9876543210

14. It's In The Bag
He puts five pennies into five of the bags, then he puts all five bags into the sixth bag!

16. Well Balanced
= 11
= 111
= 1,111
= 11,111
= 111,111
= 1,111,111
= 11,111,111
= 111,111,111
= 1,111,111,111

17. Pieces of Eight
41,312,432 (or, the number reversed, 23,421,314).

20. Time Trip
1881

21. Top Marks

24. Join the Dots

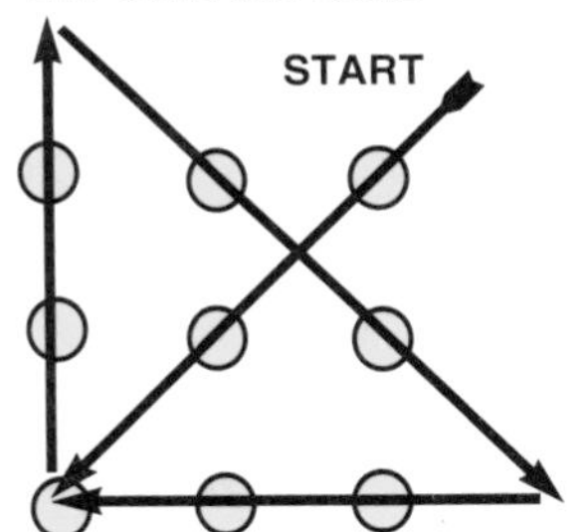

26. Code Buster
a) Luxembourg,
b) Belgium,
c) Netherlands,
d) Denmark,
e) France, f) Finland,
g) Italy. Finland is the odd one out - it's the only country listed that is not a member of the European Community.

27. Clockwise
10.15

28. More Numbers
Six - the three numbers on each card add up to 19

31. Trick Question
The trick is to use Roman Numerals - thus, XIX, take away I = XX, or 20!

32. Find the Missing Number
Ten

33. You're A Genius!
1) A = 8, B = 1 2) 6 3) XXII (23) 4) 300

34. Magic Star

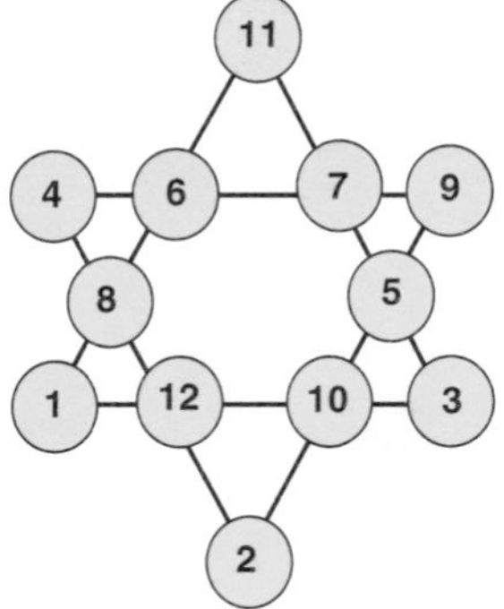

35. Magic Square

1	15	4	14
12	6	9	7
13	3	16	2
8	10	5	11

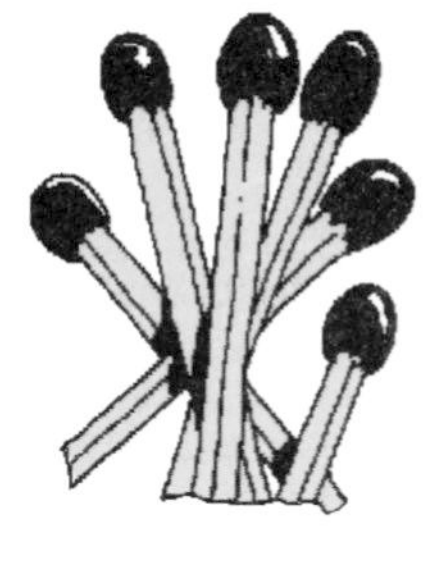

36. Vanishing Squares

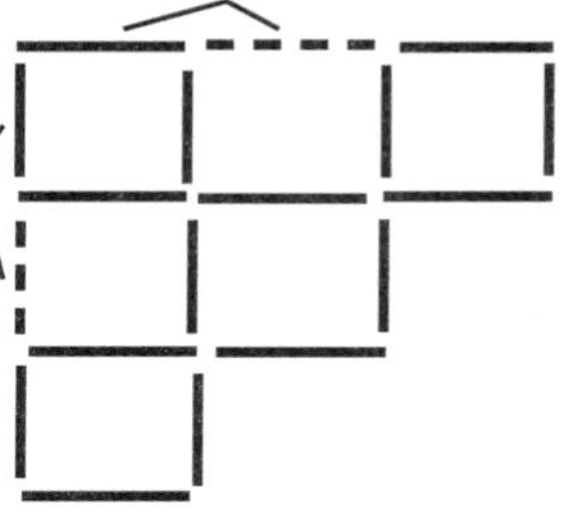

37. Magic Seven
Eight.Seven daughters and one son.

38. Square Magic

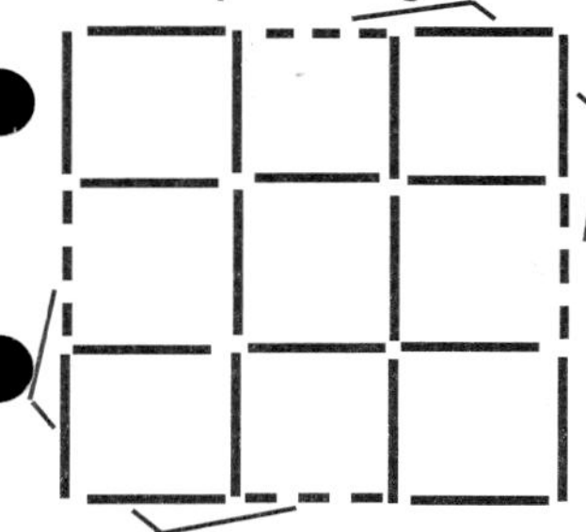

39. Number Fun

$$\begin{array}{r} 316 \\ 253 \\ +\ 847 \\ \hline 1416 \end{array}$$

40. Multiplication Magic

We have 24 x 13 = 312
We cannot have 2 incorrect digits.
Therefore 377 is retained.

Now $\frac{377}{24} = 15.7083$
Therefore, 13 is retained.
Finally, $\frac{377}{24} = 29$
The multiplication would be correct if **4** is replaced with **9**.

41. Magic 6 and 9

9969	6666	9699	6996
9696	6999	9966	6669
6966	9669	6696	9999
6699	9996	6969	9666

42. Magic Square 5 x 5

17	24	1	8	15
23	5	7	14	16
4	6	13	20	22
10	12	19	21	3
11	18	25	2	9

43. Upside Down Magic

8018	1886	6169	9901
6961	9109	8816	1088
9806	6068	1981	8119
1189	8911	9008	6866

44. Laughing Romans
My dog has no nose.
How does he smell?
Terrible.

46. Five's Alive
48828125

48. Backchat
A. 7108 - boil
B. 4509 - gosh!
C. 39718 - bilge
D. 3215 - size
E. 983 - beg

49. Counting Cows
There were 190 cows on the first two trips, and 225 cows on the fourth and fifth trips, which makes a total of 415 cows. So on the third trip, there were 500 - 415 = 85 cows.

50. Nine's Easy
2 x 9 = 18
3 x 9 = 27
5 x 9 = 45
6 x 9 = 54
7 x 9 = 63
8 x 9 = 72